The Geology of
Cornwall
an introduction

Robert Westwood

Tor Mark • Redruth

For further information of all the titles in this series please visit:-
www.tormark.co.uk

First published 2004 by Tor Mark
United Downs Ind Est, St Day, Redruth, Cornwall TR16 5HY
This reprint 2015
© 2004 Robert Westwood
All rights reserved
ISBN 978 085025 403 7

Printed by Booths Print, The Praze, Penryn, Cornwall TR10 8AA

The Rumps near Polzeath, cliffs formed from volcanic lava spewed out under the sea

1 Why is Cornwall so special?

Any visitor to Cornwall is left in no doubt that it is special. Cross the Tamar and signs of its ancient Celtic culture are everywhere; cars carry the Cornwall flag and place names have a uniquely melodic character.

It is not just the history and culture of its people that make Cornwall different; the very rocks of which it is made have a distinctive history.

Cornwall's geology is both complicated and fascinating. Piecing together its geological history has been a long and arduous process. Undoubtedly it has yet to yield all of its secrets to the many geologists who devote their academic life to unravelling the events that have formed this beautiful county.

So why is Cornwall so geologically special?

Cornwall's coastline is enjoyed by thousands of walkers. No doubt some of these people will have walked some of the spectacular paths in the mountains of the Alps. They may have been struck by the similarity of the rocks they saw along the way. Slaty rocks with thin layers and shiny minerals are common in both areas, as are the contorted shapes into which some of the rocks have been folded.

This may seem surprising since Cornwall's landscape is very different from that of the Alps. The difference, however, is largely one of age; walk along the rocky shores of Cornwall and you are walking on the core of an ancient mountain chain, long since worn down by the forces of erosion. In Cornwall we have an opportunity to study the rocks at the very centre of a mighty mountain chain and the cataclysmic events that led to its formation.

The granite moors and mineral veins which have been such an integral part of Cornwall's history are closely associated with the mountain building episode. This all adds up to a fascinating geological history, one every bit as interesting as the human story.

Weathered cliffs at Porthgwarra near Land's End

Steeply dipping strata at Crackington Haven

2 Some simple geology

Most of the rocks we see at the Earth's surface are sediments. They have formed from the weathering and erosion of other rocks; the debris has been deposited and later compacted into rock again. Sediments collect in river beds, on lake bottoms or as arid desert sands, but most collect on the sea bed from the vast amount of material that is brought to the sea by rivers. Soft sand, silt and mud gradually turns into solid rock, compressed by the weight of sediment above.

Animals that live in the sea die and fall to the bottom; their hard parts are sometimes preserved as fossils. Since the sea bed is largely flat, these sediments form flat layers, with the older layers at the bottom of the sequence. In mountainous regions such as the Alps we see these sediments complete with fossils thousands of metres above sea level. How is it that these rocks which formed at the bottom of the sea are now raised so high? Clearly enormous forces have been at work.

The key to understanding this is to realise that the Earth's crust is not static but constantly changing. Divided up into a number of 'plates' and powered by the heat within the Earth, parts of the crust collide, split apart and glide past each other. Continents move, oceans form and then are squashed out of existence. All this happens very slowly from a human perspective, but volcanoes and earthquakes bear witness to the huge forces involved.

One of the consequences of this movement is that some parts of the Earth's surface have witnessed many changes. At times they have been under a deep sea, at other times raised above sea level. They have been deltas and deserts, lakes and lagoons. They have been in tropical and arctic climates as the continents drifted about the surface of the Earth.

Rocks raised above sea level are weathered and eroded by water, wind and ice. Much material is taken back to the sea where it is deposited again and eventually forms part of a new sedimentary rock. A grain of sand lying on a Cornish beach may have gone through many such cycles.

Above: Steeply dippping Carboniferous slates at Sandymouth

Opposite: Banded Devonian slates at Polzeath

As two plates of the Earth's crust collide, buckles in the crust form ocean basins which, over millions of years, fill with thousands of metres of sediment. As the plates continue to close together, these sediments are folded up into mountain chains. The mountains of the Alps formed as the African plate pushed northwards into Europe.

A lot of heat is generated in these cataclysms. This melts huge parts of the crust, so that new igneous rock is formed, typically granite. Other rocks are significantly altered by the tremendous heat and pressure generated.

Cornwall's geology tells the story of one such mountain building episode. The rocks we see now in Cornwall are the eroded core of an ancient mountain chain. They originally collected in huge ocean basins, deforming as a crustal plate moved northwards. Granite and associated mineral deposits were a product of the enormous heat generated.

3 The Cornish killas

Most of the low lying areas of Cornwall are composed of grey, slaty rocks known to the Cornish miners as 'killas'. These rocks were origally soft sediments, deposited in a variety of environments on an ancient sea floor.

Around 360 to 400 million years ago, in the geological era known as the Devonian, Cornwall lay in the tropics south of the Equator. While much of Britain was land, south-west England lay on the edge of an ocean into which rivers brought large amounts of sediments from the erosion of mountains to the north. This general situation persisted to the end of the Carboniferous era, some 280 million years ago, by which time Cornwall had drifted north and was across the Equator.

Throughout this time Cornwall was squeezed between two colliding plates; the pressure came from the south. In the ocean, deep basins were formed as the Earth's crust buckled under the strain. Most of Cornwall's rocks originated in these basins and in the shallower ridges that separated them. Over millions of years, horizontal or near horizontal layers of sediment accumulated, thousands of metres thick.

Each change in conditions resulted in slightly different sediments being deposited. This is the reason sedimentary rocks appear as distinct layers, some harder than others, some a different colour. Generally, sediments nearer the shore are coarser grained than those deposited further out because river and coastal currents drop the larger particles first, whereas the finer silt and mud is carried far out to sea. Coarse-grained sandstones are generally harder than layers of silt and mud.

Occasionally sediments lying in a shallow sea beside a deep basin were shaken by earth tremors, sending them tumbling into the abyss. As they consolidated, such 'turbidites' left tell-tale signs of their dynamic origin, jumbled layers and scour marks on the sea bed for example.

In some places bands of limestone stick out as harder layers. Limestones are sediments that contain a significant amount of calcium carbonate, the material which once formed the shells of millions of sea creatures. Dissolved by the sea water it precipitates out when the sediment is being buried by yet more sediment and helps to form the cement that bonds the rock together. The traditional test for limestone is to put a drop of dilute hydrochloric acid on the rock. If it fizzes, there must be a substantial amount of calcium carbonate present.

Above: Devonian slates at Polzeath, showing different coloured layers

Below: Church Cove, Gunwalloe, on the Lizard, where the rocks are turbidites –
sandstones formed from sediment that tumbled down from the 'shelf' into deep ocean
basins

Brightly coloured slates make an ideal material for this wall at Talland Bay

The killas of Cornwall no longer look like layers of silt, mud and sand that collected on a sea floor. Almost everywhere we see steeply dipping layers of slate that split easily into flat segments.

This transformation was caused by the enormous earth movements associated with the collision of two plates. The heat generated baked the sediments while the tremendous pressure resulted in the typical slaty cleavage, causing the flat clay minerals to align themselves parallel to one another.

We can still see traces of the original sedimentary structures, in particular the variation in colour from black to green to purple. These changes are representative of different types of sediment laid down on the ancient sea bed. Similarly, harder layers of sandstone sometimes stand out. The enormous pressures also folded and contorted the sediments and we see examples of this in many localities.

Occasionally the slate formations contain layers of volcanic deposits, perhaps ash that poured out of a volcano or 'pillow' lavas that bubbled out of a submarine volcano and cooled quickly into lumps or 'pillows'. This activity is further evidence of the earth movements that were to shape the landscape.

No mention so far has been made of fossils. Cornwall is not noted as a prime location for collecting fossils in the way that the Jurassic Coast is. There are two main reasons. Firstly, relatively few fossils accumulated in the sediments formed in deep ocean basins because most sea life is concentrated on the shallower continental shelf. Secondly, the tremendous earth movements have squeezed and baked the sediments into slates, often obliterating traces of fossils.

However, fossils are to be found in certain locations. Fossil fish, for example, are found in the Devonian slates of the south coast: Portwrinkle is a prime location. On the north coast the Carboniferous slates around Bude contain fossiliferous bands with ammonoids, coiled shells of creatures similar to ammonites. In quarries near Launceston ammonoids, trilobites and other shell fossils called brachiopods have been found.

The sequence of sediments in Cornwall, and their relative ages, has had to be painstakingly worked out using the often meagre fossil remains.

Steeply dipping slates at the entrance to Polperro harbour

A small waterfall plunges off the Carboniferous slates at Sandy Mouth

4 Mountain building

Mountain ranges form some of Nature's most spectacular creations. Precipitous peaks made out of material that collected on the sea floor rise thousands of feet above sea level. The flat layers that once typified the sedimentary rocks are contorted into incredible folds and the sediment is baked and squashed.

Although much of Cornwall is now gentle, rolling countryside, it was once part of an impressive range of mountains. All that remains is the eroded core. It is not hard to see the evidence for this in the rocks. Examine the slate on much of Cornwall's coastline and it looks as though it has been crushed and mangled. Contorted and folded layers are prominently displayed at places like Millook Haven.

Slate was once fine grained sediment – silts and muds. The clay minerals that comprise most of these rocks naturally occur as flat crystals. When they are subjected to intense pressure they orientate so as to lie at right angles to the direction of pressure. This creates the typical slaty cleavage which results in the rock easily splitting into flat chunks.

So how do mountains form? The simple answer is that this happens when two 'plates' of the Earth's crust collide, squashing up the rocks caught between them.

From the beginning of the Devonian period around 400 million years ago to the end of the Carboniferous period roughly 280 million years ago, much of Devon and Cornwall consisted of a series of ocean basins into which sediment from neighbouring land was pouring. These basins were being gradually squashed by a continental plate to the south that was moving northwards. Giant faults or planes of weakness usually separated these basins.

The folding did not all happen at once; it was a slow process and each ocean basin responded differently to the pressure. Huge slices of sediment were thrust northwards over younger sediments. Giant 'recumbent' folds were produced. To appreciate this, hold a piece of A4 paper flat on a table. Hold down both ends, then keeping one end fixed, gradually slide the other end towards it. The paper will fold over itself into a recumbent fold

How can solid rocks deform as if they were pieces of paper or layers of plasticene? Why don't they crumble and shatter as we might expect? We need to remember that this was a very gradual process. The rocks were deeply buried at the time and under intense pressure, and subjected to high temperatures. Under these conditions rocks can behave in a more fluid manner.

Chemical analysis of the slates can give us an idea of the conditions under which these rocks were transformed. It seems likely that as the two plates collided and the sediments were progressively buried and crushed, the muds, silts and clays that had collected in the ocean basins were subjected to temperatures of around 250-350° Celsius and pressures of around 2-4 kilobars.

It is not difficult to imagine that, as these earth movements progressed, the ocean basins were subjected to tremendous earthquakes from time to time. When this happens on the continental shelf, a great mass of sediment is often sent tumbling down the continental slope to the deep sea beyond. The rocks that result from these turbid currents are known as turbidites and they typically present a jumbled character. Good examples are seen at Church Cove, Gunwalloe on the Lizard.

The mountains that formed have long since been worn away and their rock recycled to form younger sediments, but this period of mountain building left other mountain chains that still survive to this day. The beautiful Massif Central in France is one example.

Zig-zag folds show clearly in the Carboniferous sediments at Millook Haven

Large feldspar crystals in granite at Porthgwarra

5 The coming of the granites

Bleak granite moorlands are a feature of the Cornish landscape. Dotted by prehistoric remains and associated with myths and legends, they remain enigmatic places with a stark beauty. One of the best known rock types, granite is a hard, impermeable rock that characteristically forms high, barren areas which farmers struggle to make a living on, but which draw ramblers in their thousands.

It is well known that the granite outcrops in Devon and Cornwall are the tips of a giant granite reservoir or 'batholith' that underlies South West England. Igneous rocks like granite were once molten and forced their way into and under overlying rocks by their natural buoyancy. If they reached the surface they cooled quickly, giving little time for crystals to grow, resulting in a very fine grained rock. If they cooled while still deeply buried, crystallisation took place very slowly and the final rock is coarse grained, with individual minerals easily visible. The large crystals visible in the Cornish granites indicate they cooled deep underground; they have subsequently been exposed by erosion of the rocks

Jointed, frost-shattered granite cliffs at Porthgwarra near Land's End

above. The relatively hard, resistant granite has formed upland areas as the softer sediments around it have been worn away more easily.

With modern technology it has been possible to map the extent of the Cornubian batholith, even though we can only see the tips. It varies in thickness between 10 and 20 kilometres and is between 40 and 60 kilometres wide at its base. All told it has been estimated that beneath Devon and Cornwall is about 68,000 cubic kilometres of granite. Where did this come from? Where has the enormous energy come from that has heated such a huge volume of rock to around 800°C?

The origin of granite is a fairly simple matter. Take a large slice of the Earth's crust, melt it then let it cool slowly and granite will be the end product. Its composition is representative of the composition of the top layer of the Earth; what we call the crust. The most common elements are oxygen and silicon with sodium, potassium, aluminium and calcium also much in evidence, and these form the bulk of the common minerals in granite.

The heat to melt the vast quantity of crustal material came from the collision of the two plates. Deep down, as one plate slid underneath the other, the friction generated a huge amount of heat. This melted the lower crust which became buoyant and tried to force its way upwards.

Thousands of metres of sediments were above this molten granite so despite its natural buoyancy it remained trapped deep below, thus ensuring that it cooled and solidified very slowly.

This is why the granite is coarse grained; the slower an igneous rock cools, the larger its crystals grow. Molten granite is not a homogeneous fluid; rather it is a mixture of many constituents. As it cools, some minerals crystallise out before others. Those that solidify first (with a higher melting point) will tend to form the larger, well formed crystals, while those that solidify last will fill in the gaps around the other minerals. Large crystals of the mineral feldspar are a feature of some of the Cornish granite outcrops, and it is easy to appreciate that these must have been the first to crystallise.

The formation of the granites occurred around 280–300 million years ago. They shouldered aside surrounding sediments, contorting and baking them as they did so. Over the millions of years that followed, the overlying sediments were gradually worn away, exposing the tops of the giant batholith and the altered sediments in contact with them. Resistant to the forces of erosion, the granite formed a unique, rugged landscape.

Above: Prince of Wales shaft, Minions, Bodmin Moor

6 Minerals

Cornwall is famous throughout the world for its minerals. Not economically viable now, in its heyday, Cornwall's metal-mining industry employed thousands of workers.

It is fairly obvious to even the casual observer that Cornish mining is associated with the granite outcrops. The mines are usually clustered around the edge of the granite moors and this is no coincidence; the processes that deposited the valuable minerals were related to the emplacement and cooling of the huge molten granite batholith.

As the granite solidified, hot aqueous fluids circulated around the edge of the huge intrusion, pushing their way through cracks and fissures in the surrounding rock. These fluids were often rich in metals like tin, copper, lead and zinc. As the fluids cooled, metal compounds precipitated out, forming the ore deposits. These ores occur in veins or 'lodes' which follow the path of the cracks and fissures through which the hot solutions circulated.

Lots of other minerals also precipitated out, quartz being the most common. This process is responsible for the veins of quartz we typically see cutting through the slates close to the edge of granite. Mineral veins of this type have produced most of the tin, copper, arsenic and tungsten. The economically viable veins were usually at least 200 metres long and some over a kilometre long.

Mineral deposits can also occur as fluids permeate the surrounding rock, perhaps along micro-cracks. Certain parts of this 'country rock' may be dissolved and then replaced by compounds from the fluids. These are known as replacement ore bodies and often have an irregular shape. As well as hot fluids which separated from the cooling granite, mineralisation has also been caused by percolating groundwaters.

Granite veins in slate at Cape Cornwall, demonstrating how hot fluids can penetrate surrounding rocks

These cliffs at Nanven show evidence of historic mine workings

Opposite: Wheal Coates, one of many mines in the St Agnes area

The Cornish granites have maintained a relatively high temperature due to them being rich in radioactive minerals. This made possible the circulation of groundwaters over and around the granites. These waters have selectively dissolved and precipitated mineral ores. Some of these deposits have been dated to between 5 and 30 million years after the emplacement of the granite.

As the granites were exposed by weathering, some of the mineral deposits were leached by the groundwaters and redeposited lower down, often resulting in considerable enrichment of the ore body. This type of deposit was greatly sought after by the early miners.

Sometimes mineral veins were eroded and the ore was carried away and deposited elsewhere by rivers. These 'placer' deposits were a great source of cassiterite, the chief ore of tin. This is a heavy mineral and so well suited to hydraulic separation – basically the 'panning' process of gold prospectors.

Why is it that these valuable metals were left to the end of the cooling process? They originally formed a tiny part of the mixture from which the granite solidified. It seems incredible that these metals happened to be the ones that were concentrated into workable deposits.

The answer lies in their reactivity. There is far more calcium, potassium and sodium in the Cornish granites, but these metals are very reactive. In the molten stage they quickly joined up with other elements to form the minerals which make up the great bulk of the granite. The feldspar minerals for example, which are a major constituent of granite, are composed of sodium, potassium, calcium, aluminium, silica and oxygen. Because tin and copper do not react so readily, they do not easily form minerals and are left to the end of the cooling process; fortunately for us!

Quartz veining in the slates at Polzeath – a further example of how hot fluids penetrated the surrounding rocks as the granite cooled

Serpentine rock at Kynance Cove

7 The mystery of the Lizard

No other chapter in this book is concerned with just one particular part of Cornwall. Why is it that the Lizard deserves a chapter all of its own? It has long been recognised that this charming peninsula is different from the rest of Cornwall, and even to the uninitiated observer, this difference stems from its rocks. Mantelpieces and bookcases all over the country are adorned by colourful ash trays and miniature lighthouses carved from the beautiful serpentine. This, and other rocks on the Lizard, are found nowhere else in Cornwall.

Some geologists had previously speculated that the Lizard rocks were much more ancient than the rest of Cornwall and had survived by chance, before being caught up somehow in the earth movements that formed the rest of the south-west. It now seems that these strange rocks are, after all, part of the mountain building story that has shaped the county, but they do represent an unexpected twist in the story, and as such merit their own chapter.

To understand how the Lizard rocks fit in to our geological history we need to go back to geological theory. We have seen how many of the rocks of Cornwall were deposited in ocean basins, separated by ridges and caught between two converging plates of the Earth's crust. As the plates continued to converge, so the sediments were squashed and folded, with friction deep down melting the crust and giving rise to the granite.

Ocean crust is very different from continental crust. Beneath the sediments on the ocean floor you will find volcanic rocks, typically arising from volcanoes and volcanic vents along the ridges which bisect all the major oceans. This is how the plates of the crust move. The relentless volcanic activity gradually forms more oceanic crust and widens the oceans. Continental crust by contrast is formed as plates collide and material is crushed and folded up between them.

The rocks of the Lizard complex are now recognised as being a section of oceanic crust. It seems that as one of the ocean basins was being closed by the pressure of colliding plates, a piece of the ocean crust became detached and was pushed up and over sediments lying to the north of it. No wonder the Lizard rocks look different from those in the rest of Cornwall!

Kynance Cove

*Kennack Sands
on the Lizard.
A lava dyke
cuts across
other rocks*

What is even more exciting to the geologist is that here, exposed on land, we see the very base of the Earth's crust and the junction with the layer beneath, known as the mantle.

Essentially the rocks of the Lizard are igneous, that is, like granite they have solidified from a molten state. Their chemical composition is very different from granite, however, reflecting their origin from deeper within the Earth. They have been altered or metamorphosed as they were caught up in the great earth movements.

What should we look for when visiting the Lizard? In Kynance Cove we see the classic example of the serpentine. This is actually the name of a mineral. The rocks here were once part of the very bottom layer of ocean crust. The main minerals of this rock have reacted with water as temperatures rose to between 300 and 500°C to form serpentine. At various places on the Lizard, but perhaps most prominently at Porthoustock, are igneous dykes. These are vertical sheets of volcanic rock, intruded into surrounding rock.

There is not the space here to go into detail about the geology of the Lizard. Simply enjoy looking at these colourful rocks and try to pick out details that reveal their fiery and dramatic origin – sheets of volcanic lavas that have pushed aside other rocks, veined rocks and patterns that above all indicate a formation via a liquid state.

Pebbles and boulders on the beach at Kennack Sands testify to the once fluid nature of these rocks

Pillow lava at
Pentire Head
near Polzeath

8 After the mountain building

In the late Carboniferous period (around 300 million years ago) Cornwall lay across the equator. The series of ocean basins in which most of Cornwall's rocks were deposited were being deformed as a continental plate pushed northwards, closing the ocean and raising giant mountains. It did not happen suddenly but over millions of years, creating complex structures unique to each basin. This is how the giant supercontinent of Pangaea was formed, encompassing all of the Earth's landmasses.

At the end of the Carboniferous, massive granite bodies known as 'plutons' were pushing their way into the sediments above them. Associated volcanic activity saw lavas extruded on the surface. Cornwall now lay about 10° north of the equator and began to experience a hot desert climate that lasted for about 70 million years. The landscape was rugged. Continued tensions in the Earth's crust led to a number of basins forming between the mountains. These were filled with red sediments washed down from the surrounding highlands. Gradually the mountains that had formed from the continental collision were worn down. Early on in this period the fluids surrounding the still hot granites were responsible for the main mineralisation.

At Cape Cornwall the meeting point between the black slate and the light coloured granite is clearly visible

Around 200 million years ago, at the end of the Triassic period, Cornwall had drifted further north of the equator, into the tropics. The climate was now less harsh and there would have been considerable seasonal rainfall. This no doubt contributed considerably to the continuing erosion. The sea had by now returned to much of what is now southern England, leaving Cornwall as part of a low-lying island. This island included Devon, and also extended south-westwards from Cornwall. Later on in the Jurassic period (around 150 million years ago) a period of uplift and consequent fall in sea level left a much bigger landmass, extending to Ireland. A period of quite vigorous erosion was initiated.

During all this time much had been going on in the granites, still deeply buried at the core of the Cornish landmass. At the end of the Permian period and the beginning of the Triassic, around 250 million years ago, the granite had completely crystallised. It was still buried to a depth of around 1km and was still hot. This heat, however, came from the decay of radioactive minerals, and provided the energy for the circulation of fluids around and within the granites. It is these fluids that were mainly responsible for the alteration of feldspar in the granite to kaolin (china clay). This process has carried on to the present day; the radioactive minerals continue to provide a source of heat.

Just over 50 million years ago in the Cretaceous period the sea returned once more to Cornwall. This was the famous chalk sea that covered much of southern England. In its clear, tropical waters calcium carbonate from tiny sea creatures slowly accumulated to form the pure white limestone. Later earth movements, which culminated in the formation of the Alpine mountain chain, subsequently raised Cornwall once more; erosion has since removed all trace of the chalk.

Much of Cornwall has been land ever since and the continued erosion has exposed the enigmatic and contorted base of the ancient mountain range with its core of granite. The finishing touches to this unique and beautiful landscape were provided by the proximity of the Pleistocene ice sheets and the consequent changes in sea level.

Golitha Falls on Bodmin Moor, where the River Fowey continues to erode the granite

9 Up to and including the last Ice Age

During the earth movements that formed the Alpine mountain chain Cornwall was subjected to pressures and stresses that resulted in many changes in sea level. Few deposits remain from the seas that intermittently covered parts of the county.

Towards the end of the Tertiary period the sea level was some 120 metres higher than at present. The shelf that the sea eroded is a well known feature in west Cornwall, now a plain sloping gently down to the sea. It is even more evident in the Lizard where the even, flat landscape represents this ancient sea floor.

Subsequent earth movements raised more of Cornwall out of the sea and led to the rejuvenation of many river valleys. This is where a river cuts more deeply down into its valley following an increase in gradient. Many of the steep sided Cornish valleys are a product of this event. The raised beaches that are in evidence around much of Cornwall's coastline are also a product of these periods of uplift and subsequent depression. Sediments in other areas of southern England confirm that the Tertiary period was a time of frequent, relatively small earth movements, fringe effects of the Alpine mountain building episode.

The Lizard plateau represents an ancient sea floor, seen here above Kynance Cove

The Cheesewring, at Minions on Bodmin Moor

The events during and immediately after the last Ice Age, although very recent and short lived compared to the ancient earth movements previously discussed, have nevertheless been very important in shaping the landscape we see today.

Helford River, one of many river valleys drowned after the last Ice Age as the ice sheets melted and sea level rose

No glaciers or ice sheets scoured Cornwall's hills and valleys, but the ice was only a short distance away, probably reaching as far as a line between London and Bristol as recently as 18,000 years ago.

Cornwall would have been a frozen wasteland of permafrost, just as much of Siberia is today. Frost shattered the rocks and in the intervening warmer periods, the frozen ground slowly melted, resulting in slow-moving landslides of mud, grit and broken rocks. The product of these is known as glacial 'head' and is a common feature of many Cornish valleys.

When the Ice Age ended, Cornwall stood much higher than it does today. As the climate improved, melt-water swelled the rivers which swept all fine material out of their valleys and estuaries, leaving only coarse gravels resting on a rocky base. In these gravels there had sometimes accumulated pebbles bearing tin and wolfram which were too heavy to be carried away. Nature had conspired once again to concentrate important materials, to the benefit of Cornish miners.

Rock on the Camel estuary, another example of a flooded river valley or 'ria' created by the rise in sea level after the last Ice Age

The melting of the great ice sheets led to a significant rise in sea level. Other parts of the country, relieved of their great burden of ice, 'bounced' back upwards, but in Cornwall the period since the last Ice Age has been one of submergence. Rivers now once again deposited fine material, often covering the coarse tin-bearing gravels.

The inundation of forests resulted in valley peat being formed, another burden for the enterprising miners to remove. The gradual submergence of the land formed the rocky havens on the north Cornish coast and the beautiful drowned river valleys or rias of the south coast. While these have provided wonderful safe anchorage for ships, they greatly hindered communication over land.

The uniquely beautiful Cornish landscape has been the result of many complicated geological processes over millions of years. It is a landscape that has both delighted and provided for those who live, work and holiday here. A little understanding of these processes can only add to the beauty.

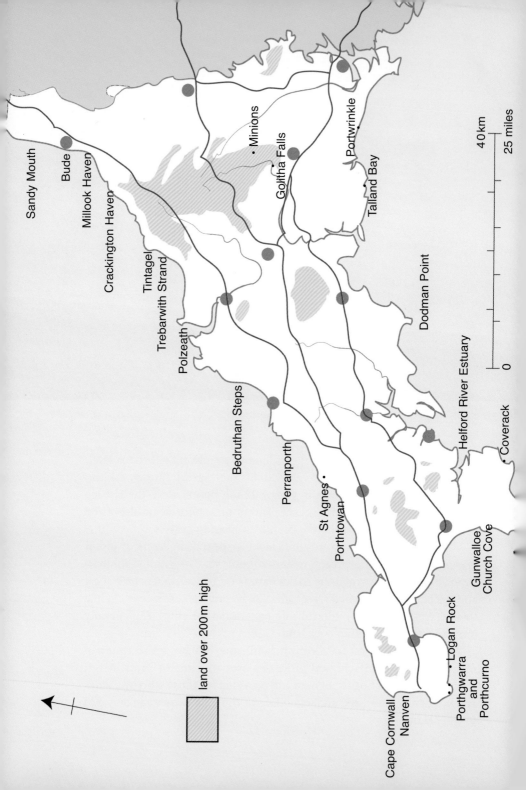

The view from Tintagel Castle

10 Places to visit

This is by no means a comprehensive list of places of geological interest. I have sought to suggest some well known locations around the county which the interested visitor, with no or little geological knowledge beyond that outlined in this book, will be able to appreciate and enjoy. They are also largely the places that feature in this book. I have organised this section by location rather than by geological episode.

North Coast

Sandy Mouth and Bude. Here are wonderful coastal sections in the Carboniferous slates or Culm Measures. The slates are typically steeply dipping, the result of compression and folding during the mountain building episode.

Millook Haven. A steep and tricky drive down to this quiet, secluded little pebble beach but well worth it. Beautiful zig-zag folds are visible in the cliff face. The slate here is intermingled with harder bands of sandstone and it is these that help pick out the folds.

Crackington Haven. Again we have steeply dipping Carboniferous slates, but look out for the recumbent folds in the cliffs.

Tintagel. The cliffs here are partly slate and partly volcanic lavas. The hard lavas have helped create a magnificent, rugged coastline. Nearby Rocky Valley is a good example of a steep sided river valley scoured out by the action of a rejuvenated stream as sea level fell.

Trebarwith Strand. The bed of the stream here is made of volcanic rocks which have been wonderfully pot-holed by the stream.

Polzeath. Upper Devonian slates are exposed at Polzeath. The rocks here often show contorted veins of quartz associated with the emplacement of the granite. Pentire Head is formed from volcanic lavas and good examples of pillow lavas can be seen. These get their name from their appearance. They formed from the rapid cooling of lava as it was extruded under the sea.

Watergate Bay. Dartmouth slates from the Lower Devonian are here folded into an anticline or upturned fold. Remember that the slaty cleavage or preferred splitting direction has formed at right angles to the direction from which the pressure came. Look for places where the strata (often distinguished by different colours) cut across this cleavage. This happens near the apex of the folds. At nearby Bedruthan Steps the slates have been eroded into spectacular sea stacks.

Perranporth. Once again the cliffs are Devonian slates but the real interest here is the huge area of blown sand, a geologically recent deposit.

St Agnes. On the cliffs between St. Agnes and Porthtowan are the Wheal Coates mine workings. In a dramatic location, these mines once employed 138 men and lodes were worked at depths of nearly 200 m.

Around Land's End

Cape Cornwall. Here is the junction between the granite and the surrounding rocks into which it has pushed. The slates of the 'host' rock have been baked by the heat of the granite. On the beach are many boulders showing how the two rock types have mixed when fluid.

Nanven. The cliffs here are full of old mine adits. There is also a good example of a raised beach covered with glacial 'head'. It is all clearly explained by a neat sign.

Granite boulders line the water's edge at Cape Cornwall

Porthgwarra. A charming cove with spectacular granite cliffs to the north and south. The jointing in the weathered granite is well displayed here.

Porthcurno. An important spot in the history of world-wide communications. Just east of here is Logan Rock, one of the most famous rocking stones caused by the weathering of the granite.

The Logan Rock at Treen, just east of Porthcurno near Land's End

The Lizard Peninsula

Church Cove, Gunwalloe. Devonian turbidites are displayed here. These are sandstones that have been deposited as material slumped down into deep marine basins from the continental shelf – perhaps displaced by earthquakes associated with the collision of crustal plates.

Kynance Cove. This is the place to see the beautiful serpentine rock. Its name is given by the mineral serpentine and it was once part of the mantle, the layer beneath the Earth's crust. Caught up by the giant earth movements, it has been crushed, heated and thrust over other rocks. The serpentine has resulted from the alteration of the original minerals through the heat and pressure.

Coverack. Walk along the beach here and you pass what was once the junction between the crust and mantle, sometimes known as the Mohorovicic Discontinuity or Moho.

Kennack Sands. This is a wonderful place for those interested in geology. The igneous rocks here have been altered into fantastic shapes and colours. Known as gneiss, a term given to rocks which have undergone a certain type of metamorphism, they show how rocks can mix and flow when in a fluid state.

Helford River. This is a beautiful example of a drowned river valley or ria, formed when the sea level rose after the Ice Age. What were once tributaries of the river are now tidal creeks.

Kennack Sands on the Lizard, a superb place for viewing rocks which have been squeezed and melted into fantastic patterns

Talland Bay, between Polperro and Looe

South Coast

Dodman Point. This rocky outcrop is made of resistant igneous rocks known as phyllites.

Fowey. Another excellent example of a ria, now a busy harbour.

Talland Bay. Devonian slates form this pretty bay and the neighbouring fishing harbour of Polperro. They dip almost vertically and display a range of colours, creating a beautiful effect.

Bodmin Moor

Minions. Near the village of Minions, north of Liskeard, is the famous Cheesewring. This tor is a perfect place to see the effects of frost-shattering on the exposed granite. Nearby are the remains of old mine workings, demonstrating the association of the mineral deposits with the emplacement of granite.

Golitha Falls. The river tumbles over granite boulders and reminds us that Cornwall has been subject to millions years of erosion that have removed thousands of metres of sediments back into the sea.